Curriculum Visions

Spelling
Book 5

Sarah Lindsay

Curriculum Visions
Spelling

Teacher's Resource Book
There is a Teacher's Resource Book to accompany this Pupil Book.

Dedicated Web Site
There's more information about other great Curriculum Visions resources and a wealth of supporting material available at:
www.CurriculumVisions.com

Author
Sarah Lindsay

Art Director
Duncan McCrae

Senior Designer
Adele Humphries

Editors
Robert Anderson and Gillian Gatehouse

Illustrations
Mark Stacey

Designed and produced by
EARTHSCAPE EDITIONS

Printed in China by
WKT Company Ltd

This product is manufactured from sustainable managed forests. For every tree cut down at least one more is planted.

First published in 2006 by Atlantic Europe Publishing Company Ltd

Text copyright © Sarah Lindsay 2006

The right of Sarah Lindsay to be identified as the author of this work has been asserted by her in accordance with the Copyright, Designs and Patents Act 1988.

Illustrations and design copyright © 2006 Atlantic Europe Publishing Company Ltd

Curriculum Visions Spelling Book 5
A CIP record for this book is available from the British Library.

ISBN-10: 1-86214-514-8
ISBN-13: 978-1-86214-514-6

Contents

Unit 1
ch

choir

chocolate

chalk	chaos	approach	chrysalis
cheese	character	mischief	orchestra
chicken	choir	ostrich	stomach
children	chorus	research	synchronise
chocolate	school	sandwich	technology

Finding words

A Write a word from the word list that matches each picture.

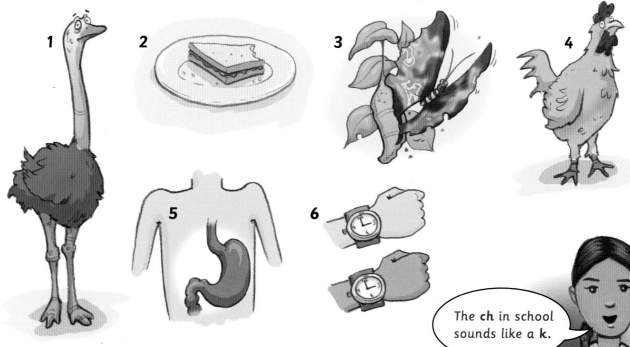

The **ch** in school sounds like a **k**.

B Say aloud the words you have written.
Write the three words where the **ch** makes a **k** sound.

4

Using words

A Copy the table. Add each of the **ch** words into the correct column.

technique

mischief

synchronise

monochrome

flowchart

trench

exchange

research

chorus

chaos

Words with **ch** as in **torch**	Words with **ch** as in **school**

Recognising similar words from the same word family can help your spelling.

technical

technology

technique

B For each word below write two more words from the same word family.

1 choose   2 chemical

Puzzle corner

Usually, when a word ending in **ch** is written in its plural form, **es** is added.

Practising plurals!

A Write each of these words in their plural form.

1 peach   2 porch   3 watch   4 switch
5 ostrich   6 bench   7 stitch   8 coach

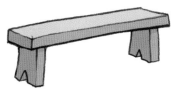

B Write four more words that end in **ch** and need **es** added when written in their plural form.

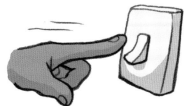

Unit 2

ent
ence

obedient

silence

science

agent	**f**ence	**differ**ent	**experi**ence
event	**p**ence	**excell**ent	**lic**ence
invent	**sci**ence	**frequ**ent	**pres**ence
moment	**sent**ence	**obedi**ent	**refer**ence
present	**sil**ence	**transpar**ent	**sequ**ence

Finding words

A Copy the sentence, filling each gap with a word from the word list.

1 The secret _____ knew his cover would be blown if he answered the phone.
2 After Manjit had taken her dog to dog training for a few months, the dog was very _____.
3 Terry was really pleased with his birthday _____.
4 Anis quickly solved the number _____.
5 Hannah peered over the _____.
6 Rick and his family were _____ visitors to the local swimming pool.

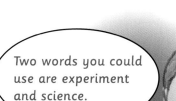

B Write a sentence or sentences describing the picture at the top of the page. Include in your writing as many **ent** or **ence** words as possible.

Two words you could use are experiment and science.

Using words

A Make two words by adding **ent** and **ence** to the letter strings.
Copy and complete the table.

	+ ent	+ ence
differ		
sil		
intellig		
evid		
obedi		
innoc		
consequ		

B Write two sentences, each with a pair of words you have made in the table.

Like this... The police were collecting more and more evid**ence** against the burglar, and it was evid**ent** he would soon be caught.

Puzzle corner

Rewrite this short passage. Spell all the words correctly!
Underline the words you change.

David was bored. It was poring with rain outsid and the wind was gusting. Suddnly, their was a huge crash and he dived for cover under the table. Eventully, when he felt a little braver he piered over the table to discuver he was now siting in the middle of a tree!
A squirel, looking as stuned as David, looked at him for a sekond and then ran of thorough the branchs. David could here his mother calling... Maybe the day wasn't going to be boreing affter all!

Have you managed to spot all seventeen spelling mistakes?

7

Unit 3

ant
ance

giant

dance

elephant	balance	arrogant	appearance
giant	dance	extravagant	distance
important	entrance	hesitant	guidance
instant	France	reluctant	performance
plant	glance	significant	substance

Finding words

A Match an ant or ance word from the word list to each of these synonyms.

1	look	glimpse
2	huge	massive
3	unwilling	unenthusiastic
4	steadiness	stability
5	show	act
6	bigheaded	proud

Just in case you have forgotten... a **synonym** is a word with the same or very similar meaning to another word.

B Write four antonyms, each for a word found in the word list.

An **antonym** is a word with the opposite meaning to another word.

Using words

A Make two words by adding *ant* and *ance* to the letter strings.
Copy and complete the table.

	+ant	**+ance**
dist		
ignor		
assist		
import		
eleg		
fragr		
extravag		

B Change each of these words into adverbs by adding
the suffix **ly** to each of them.

    1 important   **2** elegant
    3 extravagant   **4** abundant

Use each of these words in a sentence.

> An **adverb** usually describes
> a verb. It can also describe an
> adjective or another adverb.

Puzzle corner

A Write what you think each
of these expressions means.

    1 to face the music
    2 to let the cat out of the bag
    3 to take the bull by the horns
    4 to sit on the fence
    5 to put on a brave face

B Write three more expressions you
either use or might have heard.

Unit 4

auto
bi

autograph

bicycle

autocue   bicycle   autobiography   biannual
autograph   biceps   automobile   bilingual
automatic   biplane   autopilot   binoculars

Finding words

A Add the prefix auto or **bi** to make the word shown in each picture.

1 ___cycle

2 ___graph

3 ___ceps

4 ___cue

5 ___noculars

6 ___mobile

B What do you think the prefixes auto and **bi** mean?

Remember... when a prefix is added to a word it can change its meaning.

Using words

A Copy each of these words. Underline the root of each word.

1 bicycle   **2** autograph   **3** biplane

4 biannual   **5** autopilot   **6** bilingual

B Some of the root words you have underlined can have other prefixes added to them.

How many new words can you write using the root words in **A**?

> Here is one suggestion... 'telegraph'.

Puzzle corner

> I love spaghetti!

Many words we use end in vowel letters. Most of these end in **e**, but there are some words that end in **a**, **i**, **o** and **u**.

Most of these words have been borrowed from other countries.

Write a word for each of these pictures. They all end in a vowel letter (other than the letter **e**).

1

2

3

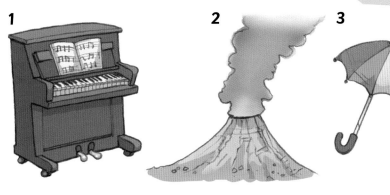

> Remember, if you aren't sure how to spell a word check it in a dictionary.

4

5

6

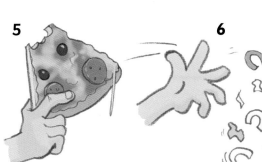

Unit 5
ly

loudly

tearfully

bravely	*feebly*	angrily	accidentally
loudly	gently	happily	humorously
quickly	simply	noisily	immediately
silently	carefully	sleepily	occasionally
tearfully	tunefully	wearily	thoughtfully

Finding words

Which adverb do you think best describes these verbs.

Copy and complete the sentences. You can only use each adverb once!

All the adverbs can be found in the word list.

1 David yawns _____.

2 Manjit shouts _____.

3 Tom runs _____.

4 Aimee writes _____.

5 Kyle yells _____.

6 Jessica swims _____.

7 Tuhil sings _____.

8 Meena plays _____.

Using words

A Look at these pairs of words.

Copy the words and then circle the adverb and underline the verb.

1 complained   hopefully   2 angrily   yelled
3 sighed   wishfully   4 fiercely   accused
5 cheekily   chuckled   6 exclaimed   scornfully

B Now use each of these pairs of words in a **dialogue** sentence.

Dialogue…
a conversation between two or more people.

Puzzle corner

When writing words in their plural form it is worth remembering… for most words that end in a **consonant** and then **y**, we drop the **y** and add **ies**.

A Change each of these words into its plural form.

1 baby   2 lady   3 lily

4 boy   5 pony   6 country

B Write four more words in their plural form that end in **ies**.

Unit 6

tele
trans
circum

telescope

transport

circumference

telegraph	transfer	telegram	circumference
telephone	transit	telepathy	circumnavigate
telescope	transmit	televise	circumstance
television	transport	transatlantic	circumstantial

Finding words

A Add the prefix **tele**, **trans** or **circum** to make the word shown in each picture.

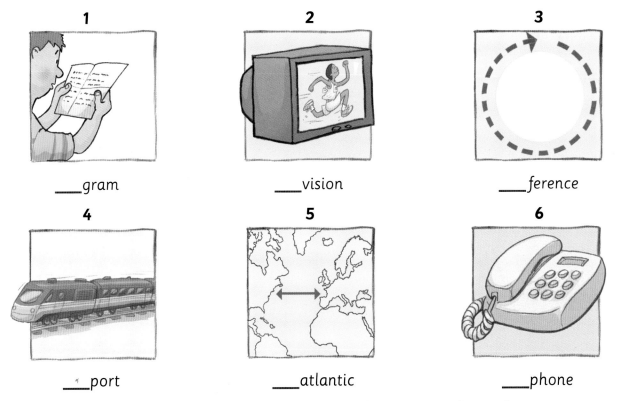

1

___gram

2

___vision

3

___ference

4

___port

5

___atlantic

6

___phone

B Choose three of the words you have just made. Write each word in a sentence.

Using words

A Write the words and their correct definitions.

1	transport	a tube-shaped instrument with a lens that makes things appear closer
2	telegram	to send something to a different place or person
3	circumnavigate	the condition in which something happens
4	telescope	to sail completely around
5	transmit	a message delivered by telegraph or hand
6	circumstance	the moving of goods or people from one place to another

B Now choose four of the words and use each in a sentence.

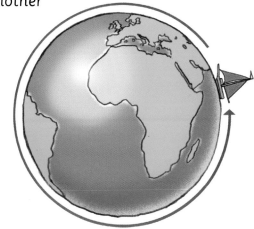

Puzzle corner

A All the words in **1** are **synonyms** of the word 'angry'.

Order the words, from those that express the least emotion to those that express the most. Do the same for the list of synonyms in **2**.

1   cross   snappy   annoyed

furious   grumpy   wild

2   jolly   cheerful

satisfied   overjoyed

merry   pleased

Remember... **synonyms** are words with the same or very similar meanings.

B Which word are the words in **2** all synonyms for?

15

Unit 7

words to watch

queue

AUDITIONS HERE TODAY

appear	different	experience	definite
careful	exciting	extremely	mischievous
finish	queue	necessary	particularly
friend	receive	recognise	ridiculous
library	vegetable	separate	vicious

Finding words

A Each of these short words can be found in a word from the word list. Write the longer word and then underline the short word found in it.

> If you find short words in longer words it can often help you spell a word.

appear	→	ap**pear**

1 table   **2** bra

3 are   **4** end

5 cog   **6** fin

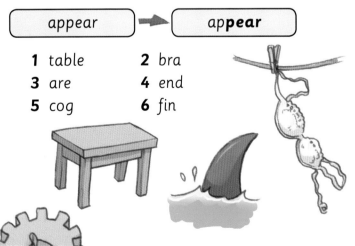

B Write all the short words you can find in each of these longer words.

    1 separate   **2** particularly   **3** different

Using words

A Each of these words has a letter missing.
Write the word, filling in the gap with the correct letter.

1 for_st   **2** We_nesday   **3** veg_table

4 tomato_s   **5** sk_ing   **6** rest_urant

7 p_jamas   **8** marg_rine   **9** light_ing

B Now check each word you have just written in a dictionary.

Tick the words you spelt right.
Rewrite the words correctly if you spelt them wrong.

h	o	f	a	v	e	s
a	s	p	h	l	s	h
v	t	h	i	e	f	e
f	b	k	d	a	p	l
p	h	o	o	f	k	f
c	a	l	f	g	d	s
a	o	f	s	b	f	h

Puzzle corner

For most words that end in **f**, we often drop the **f** and add **ves** when writing them in their plural form.

A Find five words in the wordsearch that end in **f**.

B Write each word in its plural form.

Unit 8
silent letters
b g c

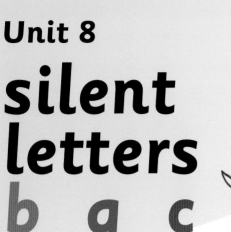

gnome

plumber

scissors

doubt	gnaw	scene	subtle
numbness	gnome	scenic	campaign
plumber	design	scent	foreign
crumb	reign	science	scenery
thumb	sign	scissors	scientist

Finding words

A Look at the picture.

List all the words with a silent letter that you can find.

The words can also be found in the word list. I can find eight words.

B Circle the silent letter in each word you have written.

Using words

A Copy the table and sort these words into their silent letters. Add two more words to each group.

debt

plumbing

diaphragm

scenery

scissors

scenario

silent b	silent g	silent c

gnat

dumbstruck

gnarled

climber

scientific

resign

You will need to think carefully about which words with silent letters you are going to choose.

B Now write two sentences.

Each sentence needs to include three words with silent letters, one with a **silent b**, one with a **silent g** and one with a **silent c**.

Puzzle corner

Write what you think these onomatopoeic words might remind you of.

Onomatopoeia means words that sound like the things they describe.

2 gurgle, gurgle

1 scrunch, rustle, snap

3 grunt, snuffle, grunt

4 pitter, patter

5 miaow, purr

6 toowit, toowoo

Unit 9
ful

colourful

mouthful

harmful

careful	colourful	doubtful	beautiful
helpful	hopeful	mouthful	bountiful
handful	harmful	shameful	dutiful
painful	powerful	thoughtful	merciful
useful	thankful	wonderful	plentiful

Finding words

A Look at each of the children. Match a word from the word list with each of them.

Challenge... You can only use each **ful** word once!

1 David is _____.

2 Manjit looks _____.

3 Tom looks _____.

4 Aimee is _____.

5 Kyle looks _____.

6 Jessica looks _____.

7 Tuhil is _____.

8 Meena is _____.

B Now draw and label someone looking shameful.

Using words

We can make **adjectives** by adding the suffix **ful** to some words.

Remember, add **ful** – not **full** – to each word.

A Add the suffix **ful** to each of these words.

1 hope	**2** mouth	**3** wonder	**4** fear
5 tear	**6** wake	**7** faith	**8** scorn

When you add **ful** to a word ending in **y**, you first change the **y** to an **i** before adding **ful**.

duty → dutiful

B Now add the suffix **ful** to each of these words.

1 beauty   **2** mercy   **3** fancy   **4** plenty   **5** pity   **6** bounty

Puzzle corner

A Add **ed** and **ing** to each of these words.

Watch out! If a word ends with a single consonant with a short vowel before it... **double** the consonant.

Like this... scrub scrub**bed** scrub**bing**

If you aren't sure what a short vowel is, ask your teacher.

knot

knit

clap

whip

trek

ship

trap

B Write three more words which need the consonant doubled when adding **ed** and **ing**.

Unit 10
letter strings

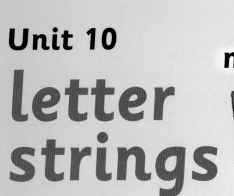
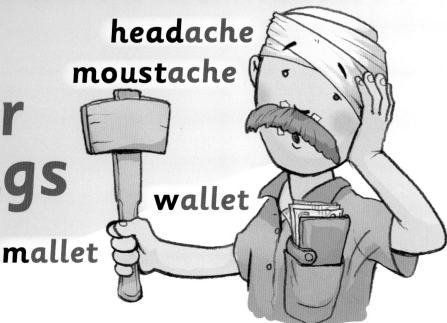

headache
moustache
wallet
mallet

dough	glove	height	headache
tough	move	weight	moustache
drought	mallet	bruise	catalogue
thought	wallet	guide	tongue

Finding words

A Look at these letter strings.
Write a word from the word list that uses the same letter string.

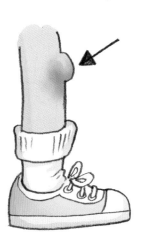

1 ui

2 allet

3 ought

4 ove

5 eight

6 gue

7 ough

8 ache

B Write an **antonym** from the word list for each of these words or phrases.

1 weak   **2** keep still   **3** flood

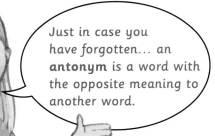

Just in case you have forgotten... an **antonym** is a word with the opposite meaning to another word.

Using words

Words can have the same letter strings but different pronunciations.

A All the words in the word list with the same letter strings have different pronunciations.

Say the words aloud.

Listen to the different sound the same letter strings can make.

Pronunciation means the way a word sounds.

B Copy the table.

Match each word in the box with a word in the table with the same pronunciation.

rough	nought	trough
plough	thorough	though

dough	tough	brought	bough	cough	borough

Puzzle corner

Sort these words into the subjects Geography, Science, History and Maths.

weather

symmetry

graph

insect

condensation

conflict

country

particles

friction

pollution

region

document

civilisation

parliament

estimate

fraction

2+2

Unit 11

soft c

circus

prince

cereal	celebrate	centimetre	electrician
circus	excellent	medicine	magician
fence	innocent	necessary	musician
parcel	peace	practice	optician
prince	recipe	sequence	politician

Finding words

A What am I?

1 I'm often the boundary between houses.
2 I guide you through cooking a dish for a meal.
3 I can help you get better when you feel ill.
4 I can be eaten for breakfast.
5 I am a unit of measurement.
6 When something is very good.
7 I can be delivered to your house.
8 A time when there is no fighting or war.

Shh... You will find the words in the word list!

B Write clues for three more **soft c** words.

Try them out on a friend.

Using words

When a **c** sounds like **s** in a word, it is called a **soft c**.

A Sort the words below into two columns.

Watch out! Some words will go in both columns.

Words with a **c** as in nice	Words with a **c** as in cat

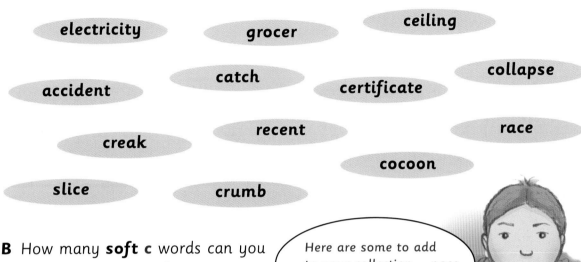

electricity   grocer   ceiling

accident   catch   certificate   collapse

creak   recent   race

cocoon

slice   crumb

B How many **soft c** words can you find ending in **ace** and **ice**?

Here are some to add to your collection... pace, palace, slice, office.

Puzzle corner

Antonyms are words that imply the opposite.
Some words have one antonym, some words have many antonyms and some words have none!

How many antonyms can you write for each of these words?
Copy and complete this table.

	Antonyms	Number of antonyms
hot		
red		
big		
near		
zoo		

Unit 12

soft g

gigantic
gem

gem	angel	generous	courage
giant	garage	gigantic	dungeon
ginger	hedge	imagine	knowledge
gipsy	magic	luggage	refugee
giraffe	stage	strange	storage

Finding words

A What am I?

1 I can mark the edge of a field.
2 I can flavour biscuits.
3 I can be found in a castle.
4 I have a very long neck!
5 I'm a precious stone.
6 I am somewhere to keep a car dry.
7 You have me when you're being brave.
8 I'm a platform from which you can entertain others.

> Again, you will find the words in the word list!

B Write clues for three more **soft g** words.

Try them out on a friend.

Using words

When a **g** sounds like **j** in a word, it is called a **soft g**.

A Find the **soft g** words in the wordsearch.

> Watch out! Not all the words you find will have a **soft g**.

g	o	a	t	e	y	c	e	o
e	s	j	s	k	d	a	j	t
n	e	s	d	h	a	b	f	j
t	g	p	y	o	t	b	e	u
l	a	o	f	h	u	a	d	f
e	t	n	k	m	a	g	i	c
y	h	g	a	r	d	e	n	s
j	e	e	u	r	g	e	n	t
o	r	g	e	r	m	s	d	k

> Have you found all six words?

B Now write each of the **soft g** words you have found in some sentences.

Puzzle corner

A Challenge… can you write a sentence that includes both of the homophones in each box?

> **Homophones** are words that sound the same but have different spellings.

1 ate   eight

2 new   knew

3 blue   blew

B List three more homophone pairs.

27

Unit 13
ure

picture

measure

capture	closure	adventure	displeasure
fixture	measure	creature	enclosure
future	pressure	departure	exposure
mixture	treasure	miniature	insure
picture	unsure	temperature	leisure

Finding words

A Copy and complete the sentences.

> Guess where the missing words can be found…!

    1 The _____ was hung on the wall.

    2 The strange _____ only came out at night!

    3 Hussain's _____ was so high, even the doctor was worried.

    4 The cake _____ looked very odd once the baked beans had been added!

    5 The football _____ had to be cancelled as the pitch had flooded.

    6 While Danielle's dad was building her a tree-house he asked her to _____ a piece of wood on the ground.

B Write a sentence to describe the picture at the top of the page. Include at least four **ure** words.

Using words

A Write a short story.

Include all the words in the treasure map!

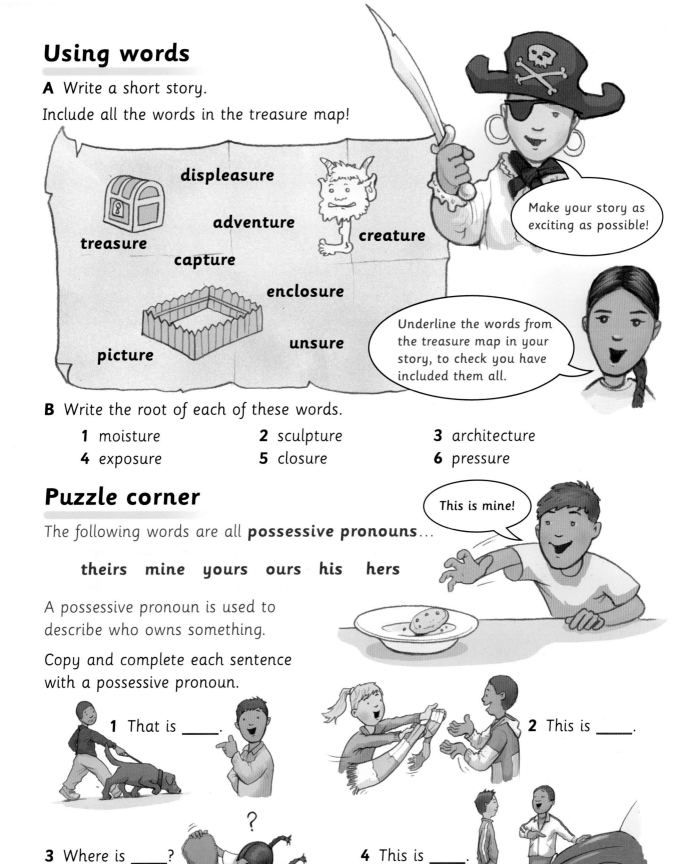

displeasure

adventure

creature

treasure

capture

enclosure

picture

unsure

Make your story as exciting as possible!

Underline the words from the treasure map in your story, to check you have included them all.

B Write the root of each of these words.

1 moisture   **2** sculpture   **3** architecture

4 exposure   **5** closure   **6** pressure

Puzzle corner

This is mine!

The following words are all **possessive pronouns**…

theirs   mine   yours   ours   his   hers

A possessive pronoun is used to describe who owns something.

Copy and complete each sentence with a possessive pronoun.

1 That is ____.

2 This is ____.

3 Where is ____?

4 This is ____.

Unit 14

al

musical

hospital

final	hospital	factual	autumnal
local	normal	magical	cathedral
medal	sandal	musical	electrical
pedal	signal	natural	occasional
royal	spiral	special	original

Finding words

A Write a word from the word list that matches each picture.

B Choose four words from the word list and write each in a sentence.

Using words

Many words that end in **al** are adjectives.

A Write these adjectives as adverbs by adding **ly** to each word.

Just add **ly**, don't change the root!

1 actual	**2** usual	**3** occasional
4 normal	**5** additional	**6** medical

B Choose three more adjectives that end in **al**.

Change each **al** word into an adverb then write each adverb in a sentence.

Watch out! Not all adjectives can be turned into adverbs.

Like this…
accidental accidentally
"Whoops, I accidentally dropped my sweets!"

Puzzle corner

Copy and complete these expressions.

Cover the words in the box. Try and complete the expressions without looking!

1 Don't beat about the _____.
2 To smell a _____.
3 To put the _____ before the horse.
4 Don't give up the _____.
5 Absence makes the _____ grow fonder.
6 To _____ your head in shame.

heart hang bush cart ghost rat

Unit 15

el

kestrel

towel

angel	barrel	channel	caramel
camel	funnel	flannel	cockerel
model	kennel	kestrel	mackerel
towel	mussel	shrivel	mongrel
vowel	tunnel	swivel	parallel

Finding words

A Look at the picture. Find nine el words from the word list.

B There are two more words ending in el hidden in the picture but these cannot be found in the word list! Can you find them?

Using words

A Add **el** or **le** to each of these letters to make a word.

1 trav__ **2** chap__

3 cand__ **4** nov__

5 kett__ **6** swiv__

7 stumb__ **8** satch__

B Use all the words you have made in a short story. How many more **el** words can you include?

Bet you can't include four more **el** words!

Puzzle corner

An **acronym** is a word or letter string made up from the initial letters of a phrase.

A Which countries are these acronyms for?

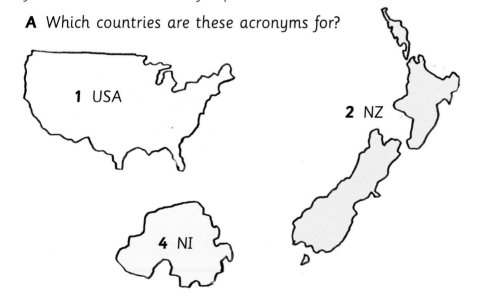

1 USA

2 NZ

3 UK

4 NI

B List three more acronyms.

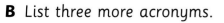

Unit 16

un
im
il

unhappy   **im**polite   **il**legal

unbroken	**un**certain	**im**patient	**il**legal
unbutton	**un**expected	**im**perfect	**il**legible
unhappy	**un**interested	**im**polite	**il**legitimate
unlimited	**un**pleasant	**im**portant	**il**literate
unusual	**un**reliable	**im**possible	**il**logical

Finding words

A Add the un, **im** or **il** prefix to each of these words. The pictures will help.

1 ___pleasant

2 ___happy

3 ___legal

4 ___patient

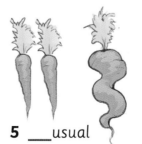

5 ___usual

6 ___possible

B Now add the un, **im** or **il** prefix to each of these roots.

    1 button   **2** polite   **3** logical   **4** legible   **5** perfect   **6** broken

Do you remember, an **antonym** is a word with the opposite meaning?

Using words

By adding the prefixes **un**, **im** and **il** you often make the **antonym** of the original word.

happy ➡ **un**happy

Check your answers in a dictionary!

A Write your own definition for each of these words.

1 imperfect   **2** unfortunate   **3** illiterate
4 unwrap   **5** impractical   **6** impure

B Copy these words and underline the root in each one.
1 illegitimate   **2** improbable   **3** unknown
4 immobile   **5** unnecessary   **6** improper

Puzzle corner

Sometimes we use words that are shortened.
Words can be shortened in a number of different ways – by...

* removing prefixes or suffixes   **telephone** ➡ **phone**

* abbreviating words   **Doctor** ➡ **Dr**

* leaving out letters   **you will** ➡ **you'll**

Copy and complete the table below by writing the words in the correct column.

Prefix/suffix removed	Abbreviation	Leaving out letters

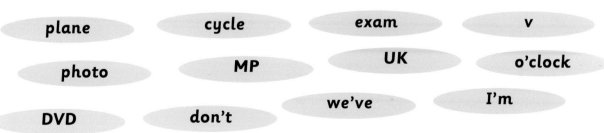

plane   cycle   exam   v

photo   MP   UK   o'clock

we've   I'm

DVD   don't

Unit 17

er
est
ish

smallish
smaller
smallest

busier   coldest   boyish   happier
cleaner   flattest   childish   muddier
funnier   merriest   largish   fussiest
hotter   sweetest   longish   spottiest
shorter   wisest   smallish   ugliest

Finding words

A Write the word from the word list that describes each picture.

B Draw your own pictures to illustrate these words.

   1 cleaner   **2** merriest   **3** longish

Using words

If you add the suffixes **er** or **est** to an adjective it can change the word into a **comparative** or **superlative**.

A **comparative** is a word that compares two things (**+er**).

A **superlative** is a word that compares three or more things (**+est**).

Do you remember...?

- If a word ends in **e** just add **r** (not er) or **st** (not est).

rude → rud**er** → rud**est**

- If a word ends in **y**, change the **y** to an **i** before adding **er** or **est**.

funny → funni**er** → funni**est**

- But... if a word has one vowel letter before the last letter, you double the last letter of the word and then add **er** or **est**.

hot → hot**er** → hot**test**

A Add **er** and **est** to each of these words.

1 pretty	**2** pale	**3** busy	**4** frail
5 healthy	**6** short	**7** sad	**8** wise

B Choose four of the pairs of words you have just made.
Write each pair of words in a sentence.

Puzzle corner

Write your own definitions for these slang words.

- **1** wicked
- **2** lush
- **3** not
- **4** gross

That's wicked!

That's great... not!

Yuck, that's gross!

Wow, he's lush!

Unit 18

ion

competition

celebration

attraction	confession	celebration	conclusion
collection	discussion	competition	decision
instruction	expression	exhibition	expansion
invention	obsession	imagination	invasion
subtraction	possession	investigation	persuasion

Finding words

Find and write the eight **ion** words hidden in the wordsearch.

e	x	h	i	b	i	t	i	o	n	t
x	k	c	s	a	o	y	t	e	a	o
p	p	e	r	s	u	a	s	i	o	n
a	t	t	r	a	c	t	i	o	n	g
n	u	d	s	i	o	s	a	d	t	d
s	e	t	u	o	t	f	k	d	e	e
i	n	v	e	n	t	i	o	n	d	c
o	e	a	s	a	e	o	i	u	o	i
n	a	s	c	u	k	n	a	e	s	s
d	i	s	c	u	s	s	i	o	n	i
d	t	i	o	n	d	g	s	j	u	o
c	o	m	p	e	t	i	t	i	o	n

Using words

When **ion** is added to a verb it often becomes a **noun.**

A Change these nouns into verbs.

1 concentration   2 calculation
3 procession   4 revision
5 infection   6 punctuation
7 television   8 intrusion
9 competition

B Change these verbs into nouns.
Use a dictionary to help you.

1 collide   2 imagine   3 persuade
4 protect   5 abbreviate   6 extend
7 divert   8 divide   9 suspend

Puzzle corner

A **thesaurus** is a book that provides **synonyms** of words.

Use a thesaurus to find a synonym for each of the bold words in these sentences.

Write the new sentence you have made. You may change some of the other words as well if you wish.

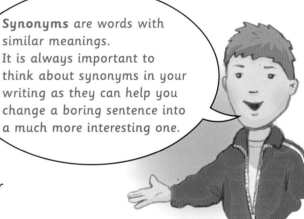

Synonyms are words with similar meanings.
It is always important to think about synonyms in your writing as they can help you change a boring sentence into a much more interesting one.

1 The **loud** noise woke Laila.
2 Ben **asked** if he could **run** to the shops.
3 Sam **pushed** his brother into the pool.
4 Tuhil **goes** to football club every week and likes it.
5 Kate **looked** for her **warm** jumper.

Unit 19

en
ify
ise

frighten

apologise

frighten	glorify	advertise	equalise
lighten	intensify	apologise	fertilise
thicken	solidify	dramatise	fossilise
tighten	simplify	magnetise	specialise

Finding words

Guess where the missing words can be found…!

A Copy and complete the sentences.

1 The headteacher decided to _____ the new football club.
2 Anya had lost weight and had to _____ her belt.
3 David tried to _____ his complicated instructions.
4 Gemma went to _____ to her teacher for knocking the paint on the floor.
5 Dad dressed up as a ghost to _____ Mum!
6 The farmer needs to _____ the poor soil in his field.

B Choose two words from the word list and write each in a sentence.

Using words

Often when the suffixes **en**, **ify** and **ise** are added to a noun or adjective, it changes it into a **verb**.

fossil → fossil**ise**

A Write the nouns or adjectives these verbs were made from.

1 advertise	**2** solidify	**3** lighten
4 magnetise	**5** dramatise	**6** economise

Use a dictionary to help.

B Write a definition for each of these words.

1 specialise
2 intensify
3 thicken
4 simplify

Puzzle corner

When a suffix that begins with a vowel is added to a word ending in a modifying or magic **e**, the **e** is **dropped**.

surpris**e** + **ing** = surpris**ing**

A Look at the picture. Can you find and write eight verbs that end in **e**?

Hint... In each word the e will need to be dropped before adding ing.

B Now add **ing** to each of the words.

Unit 20

tt

omelette

bottle

rattle

battle	attack	courgette	attention
bottle	attract	omelette	attitude
cattle	attend	palette	committee
rattle	attempt	statuette	pattern
prattle	attic	usherette	settlement

Finding words

A Write a word from the word list that matches each picture.

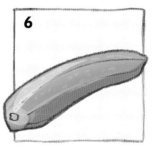

B Choose four words from the word list and write each in a sentence.

Using words

A Answer these questions with the correct **tt** word.

> **attend**   **pretty**   **cotton**   **matt**   **mutter**

1 An antonym for this word is 'glossy'.
2 I'm a material.
3 If you go to something you do this.
4 To chatter quietly on and on.
5 Add a letter to petty to make this word.

B Word challenge

1 Find three words that end in **tton**.
2 Find three words that end in **tten**.
3 Find three words by only changing the first vowel in butter.

Puzzle corner

The **tense** of a verb tells us when something is happening.

Copy and complete the table.

> Adding **ing** to a verb can change the tense of a word into the present.
> Adding **ed** to a verb can change the tense of a word into the past.

Verb	+ing present	+ed past
divide		
imagine		
exhibit		
discuss		
collide		
operate		

I am slicing the pie.

I have sliced the pie.

Unit 21

aw au

yawn

autumn

shawl

crawl	awful	author	applause
prawn	awkward	autograph	audience
straw	drawer	autumn	authority
thaw	sawdust	caught	laundry
yawn	shawl	daughter	thesaurus

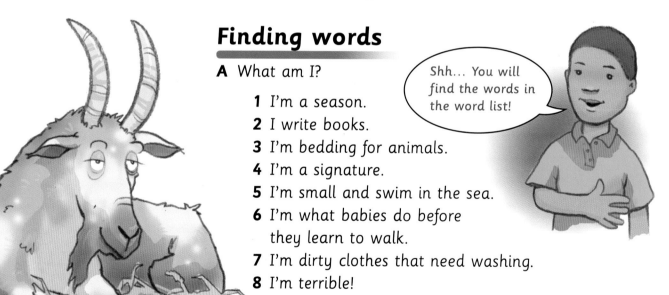

Finding words

A What am I?

1 I'm a season.
2 I write books.
3 I'm bedding for animals.
4 I'm a signature.
5 I'm small and swim in the sea.
6 I'm what babies do before they learn to walk.
7 I'm dirty clothes that need washing.
8 I'm terrible!

Shh... You will find the words in the word list!

B Write clues for three more **aw** or **au** words.
Try them out on a friend.

44

Using words

A Add the missing **aw** or **au** letters to these words.

    1 appl___se   **2** ___tograph   **3** ___kward   **4** y___n

    5 sh___l   **6** c___ght   **7** l___ndry   **8** ___dible

    9 spr___l   **10** dr___l

B Write four sentences.
Each sentence must include an **aw** and **au** word.

Here's an example!
"The **au**thor y**aw**ned as he signed even more of his books."

Puzzle corner

Some words are tricky to spell because they have a vowel letter that is hard to hear. These vowels are called **unstressed vowels**.

If you say the word 'interest', the first **e** is hard to hear. Try it!

A Say each of these words aloud.
Copy the words with unstressed vowels.
Circle the unstressed vowel in each word.

spaghetti

factory   history

camera

valuable   sandpit   nursery

marmalade   vegetable   remember

B Write three more words that contain unstressed vowels.

Unit 22

ph

phantom

pamphlet

telephone

phantom	alphabet	graph	atmosphere
pheasant	dolphin	autograph	biography
phone	elephant	paragraph	microphone
photo	pamphlet	photograph	physical
phrase	telephone	telegraph	sphinx

Finding words

A Find the word from the word list to match each picture.

B Say each word aloud.
What sound do the letters **ph** make in each word?

Using words

Many of the words that use the **ph** letter pattern originally came from the Greek language.

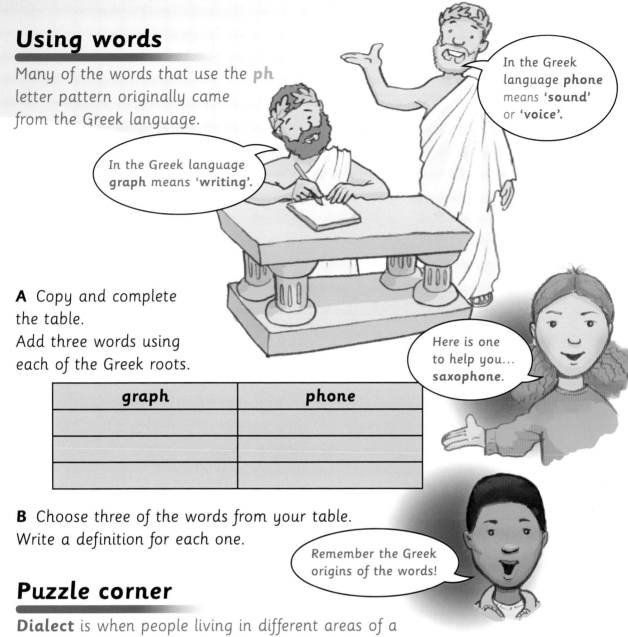

In the Greek language **graph** means '**writing**'.

In the Greek language **phone** means '**sound**' or '**voice**'.

A Copy and complete the table.
Add three words using each of the Greek roots.

Here is one to help you... **saxophone**.

graph	phone

B Choose three of the words from your table.
Write a definition for each one.

Remember the Greek origins of the words!

Puzzle corner

Dialect is when people living in different areas of a country say the same thing but in a different way.
Rhyming slang is part of the London dialect.

Match the rhyming slang with its meaning.

1 frog and toad

3 apples and pears

5 bread and cheese

2 skin and blister

4 sugar and honey

6 plates of meat

knees   **stairs**   **feet**   **money**   **road**   **sister**

Spelling Challenge

Write a word that uses each of these sounds or letter patterns.

You have practised all the sounds and letter patterns in this book!

1 ch
2 ent, ence
3 ant, ance
4 auto, bi
5 ly
6 tele, trans, circum
7 silent letters b, g, c
8 ful
9 soft c
10 soft g
11 ure
12 al
13 el
14 un, im, il
15 er, est, ish
16 ion
17 en, ify, ise
18 tt
19 aw, au
20 ph

Well done, you have now finished this book. We hope it has helped you with your spellings.